Glencoe Literature
Reading with Purpose

Unit 7 Resources
Course 3

What's Worth Fighting For? What's Not?

McGraw Hill Glencoe

New York, New York   Columbus, Ohio   Chicago, Illinois   Peoria, Illinois   Woodland Hills, California

To the Teacher

The *Unit 7 Resources: Course 3* blackline masters provide support for Unit 7 in *Glencoe Literature: Reading with Purpose.* Activities relate to and extend the themes in *Glencoe Literature: Reading with Purpose,* and include instruction, graphic organizers, and checklists to guide students through each stage of the reading and writing process.

Glencoe

Send all inquiries to:
Glencoe/McGraw-Hill
8787 Orion Place
Columbus, OH 43240-4027

ISBN-13: 978-0-07-876186-7
ISBN-10: 0-07-876186-7

Printed in the United States of America.

1 2 3 4 5 6 7 8 9 021 12 11 10 09 08 07 06

Contents

Unit Introduction
(Use with Unit Introduction, p. 922)

What's Worth Fighting For? What's Not?

What's worth fighting for? Sometimes we have to make that decision. We are faced with situations in which we must decide what is really important to us. You are going to read about characters that understand when to fight for their principles.

ACTIVITY

Look at the quotation from Alfred Adler. Then answer the following questions.

1. What does it mean to fight for a principle? Describe a time when you or someone you know fought for a principle.

_____

_____

_____

_____

2. What does it mean to "live up" to principles? Why might it be more difficult to live up to principles than to fight for them?

_____

_____

_____

_____

Discuss your answers with a partner. Then answer the following question.

3. Does the quotation mean the same thing to each of you, or does it mean something different? Explain.

_____

_____

_____

_____

_____

The Big Question—School to Home
(Use with Warm-Up, p. 924)

Unit 7 focuses on the Big Question: What's worth fighting for? What's not? You will be reading about people who are faced with that question. Before you begin to consider the Big Question, ask a parent or another adult what he or she thinks. Choose one of the following activities to complete at home.

ACTIVITY: What Is Worth It?

Ask a parent or another adult in your home to think about issues that are worth fighting for and issues that are not. For example, is a friendship worth fighting for? Is a missed appointment worth fighting for? Record the adult's responses in the chart below.

What's Worth Fighting For?	What's Not?

ACTIVITY: Changes

Ask a parent or adult to consider a time when he or she had to stand up for an important value or belief. What was the issue? What was the outcome? Was it worth fighting for? Record the adult's description in the space below.

_____

_____

_____

_____

_____

_____

(continued)

The Big Question—School to Home
(Use with Warm-Up, p. 924)

ACTIVITY: Principles to Live By

Ask a parent or another adult to consider principles and values that he or she thinks are important. For example, is honesty an important value? Ask the adult why he or she thinks each value is important. Record his or her responses in the chart below.

Value	Why Value Is Important

Read over the values that the person listed. Based on the adult's responses, write a motto, or saying, that sums up his or her values.

_____

_____

_____

_____

_____

La pregunta importante—De la escuela a la casa *(Usar con Warm-Up, pág. 924)*

La Unidad 7 se centra en la Pregunta importante: ¿Por qué cosas vale la pena luchar? ¿Por cuáles no? En esta unidad vas a leer acerca de personas que enfrentan esa pregunta. Antes de pensar en la Pregunta importante, pide a uno de tus padres o a otro adulto que te diga lo que cree. Escoge una de las tres actividades para completar en tu casa.

ACTIVIDAD: ¿Qué vale pena?

Pide a uno de tus padres o a otro adulto de tu casa que piense en cosas por las que vale la pena luchar y otras que no. Por ejemplo, ¿vale la pena luchar por una amistad? ¿Vale la pena luchar por una cita que perdimos? Anota las respuestas de esta persona en la siguiente tabla.

¿Por qué cosas vale la pena luchar?	¿Por cuáles no?

ACTIVIDAD: Cambios

Pregunta a uno de tus padres o a otro adulto que piense en una ocasión en la que él o ella tuvo que defender una creencia o un valor importante. ¿Cuál fue el problema? ¿Cuál fue el resultado? ¿Valió la pena luchar por éste? Anota la descripción de esta persona en el siguiente espacio.

_____

_____

_____

_____

(continuación)

La pregunta importante—De la escuela a la casa *(Usar con Warm-Up, pág. 924)*

ACTIVIDAD: Principios fundamentales para tu vida

Pide a uno de tus padres o a otro adulto que considere los principios y los valores que cree que son importantes. Por ejemplo, ¿es la honestidad un valor importante? Pide al adulto que te diga por qué cree que cada valor es importante. Anota sus respuestas en la siguiente tabla.

Valor	Por qué es importante el valor

Lee los valores que enumeró esa persona. Basándote en las respuestas de esa persona, escribe una frase o un dicho que resuma sus valores.

_____

_____

_____

_____

_____

Name _____ Class _____ Date _____

The Big Question Foldable
(Use with Warm-Up, p. 925)

The Big Question Foldable

(Use with Warm-Up, p. 925)

Key Reading Skill
(Use with Reading Workshop 1, p. 930)

Distinguishing Fact from Opinion

Being able to **distinguish fact from opinion** is one of the most important skills you can have as a reader. When you can tell what is fact and what is opinion, you can judge whether information can be trusted.

Remember, a **fact** is a statement that can be proved true with supporting evidence. An **opinion** is a statement that represents someone's belief or viewpoint. An opinion may be supported with evidence, but it cannot be proved true.

ACTIVITY

Reread "Tattoos: Fad, Fashion, or Folly?" on page 390. Tell whether each of the statements below is a fact or an opinion. Then explain how you figured out what the statement was.

Statement	Fact or Opinion?	How I Figured it Out
Tattooing is a passing fad.		
Tattoos mean different things in different cultures.		
Tattooing can be used to dehumanize people.		
Tattoos are just for young people.		
Getting a tattoo is always risky.		

Literary Analysis
(Use with Reading Workshop 1, p. 933)

Persuasive Appeals

Some authors try to persuade readers to agree with an opinion or to take action. An author will do this by using **persuasive appeals.** There are three main types of persuasive appeals:

- **Appeals to reason** use facts, logic, and evidence to prove a point.
- **Ethical appeals** address people's sense of good and bad, or morals. The author presents his or her position as being the "right thing to do."
- **Emotional appeals** play on emotions and are used to persuade readers to care about a topic.

ACTIVITY

Reread "A Letter to Senator Edwards" on page 927. Look for examples of persuasive appeals and write them in the following chart.

Emotional Appeals	Ethical Appeals	Appeals to Reason

Active Reading Graphic Organizer
(Use with Reading Workshop 1, p. 934)

"Saving Water: Why Save Something That Covers Two-thirds of the Earth?"

The author of "Saving Water" describes the process that water goes through to get from nature to you. Use the graphic organizer below to describe that process.

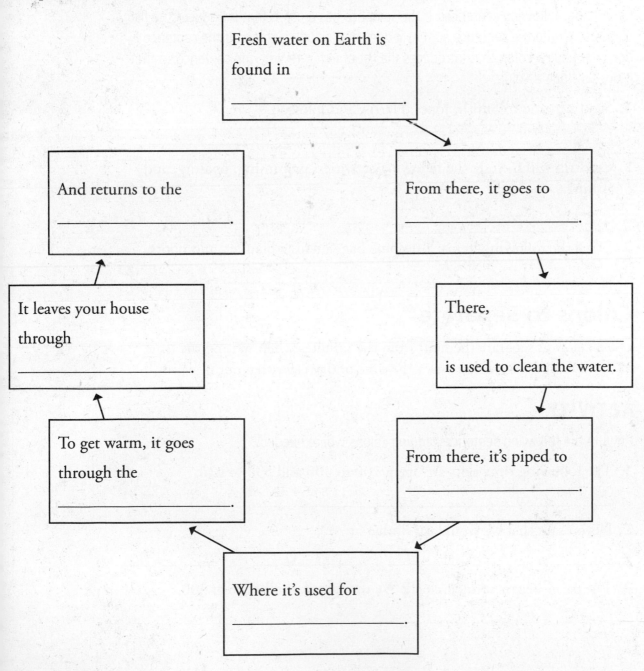

Fresh water on Earth is found in _____.

From there, it goes to _____.

There, _____ is used to clean the water.

From there, it's piped to _____.

Where it's used for _____.

To get warm, it goes through the _____.

It leaves your house through _____.

And returns to the _____.

Grammar Practice
(Use with Grammar Link, pp. 941 or 951)

Colons to Introduce Items

Use a colon to introduce a series of items at the end of a complete thought. Do not use a colon after a verb or a preposition.

ACTIVITY

Rewrite the following sentences. If the sentence has a colon that introduces the list of items, rewrite the sentence so that it does not include a colon. If the sentence does not have a colon that introduces the list of items, rewrite the sentence so that it does include a colon.

1. Send a memo to Smith, Jones, Harris, and Johnson.

_____

2. Our trip will include the following activities: swimming, boating, and fishing.

_____

3. Bring the following items: a sleeping bag, a tent, a blanket, and boots.

_____

Colons to Separate

Use a colon to separate the hour from the minutes when writing the time of day. Do not use a colon when the time of day is written out in words.

ACTIVITY

Rewrite the following sentences, adding colons where needed.

1. The following time slots are open: 200 to 400 and 530 to 630.

_____

2. Devon said that we would eat dinner at 700.

_____

3. The party began at one o'clock? We thought that it began at 200.

_____

Active Reading Graphic Organizer
(Use with Reading Workshop 1, p. 944)

from *The Measure of Our Success*

In the first part of *The Measure of Our Success,* the author describes her childhood in the rural South. In the second part, she gives you eight lessons she has learned. Use this chart to connect the lessons to her childhood experiences. Record each lesson in the small boxes. Then explain in the boxes below how each lesson relates to her life.

Lesson 1:	Lesson 2:	Lesson 3:	Lesson 4:
Lesson 5:	Lesson 6:	Lesson 7:	Lesson 8:

Writing Workshop Graphic Organizer
(Use with Writing Workshop Part 1, p. 952)

In the Writing Workshop, you are going to write a persuasive essay. In a persuasive essay, the writer tries to convince readers to agree with his or her opinions about a particular topic.

ACTIVITY

Use the graphic organizer below to help plan your essay. Because this is prewriting, you do not need to write in complete sentences. Include at least three details that support your opinion.

Topic:	
Position:	
Supporting Detail:	
Supporting Detail:	
Supporting Detail:	
Supporting Detail:	
Supporting Detail:	
Supporting Detail:	

Grammar Practice
(Use with Grammar Link, p. 955)

Apostrophes

- Use an apostrophe in a contraction to show where letters are missing.
  Example: Have not = have**n't**

- Use an apostrophe in the shortened form of a number:
  Example: The class of 1996 or The class of '96

- Use an apostrophe to show possession.
  Example: The shirt**'s** stripes were yellow.
  (The **'s** tells you that the yellow stripes belong to the shirt.)

- Follow these rules when using an apostrophe to show possession.
  Singular nouns: add **'s**
  Example: The dog**'s** collar was too loose.
  Indefinite pronouns: add **'s**
  Example: Everybody**'s** lunch included either an apple or an orange.
  Plural nouns not ending in *s*: add **'s**
  Example: The women**'s** restroom is down the hall.
  Plural nouns ending in *s*: add only an **apostrophe**
  Example: The dogs**'** owners enjoyed being at the park as much as their pets did.

- Possessive personal pronouns *(ours, yours, his, hers, its, theirs)* do not require an apostrophe.

ACTIVITY

Rewrite each sentence. Add apostrophes where needed.

1. The trees leaves fell around its trunk.

_____

2. I dont understand how the dogs leash got tangled.

_____

3. The apples skin had bruises all over it.

_____

Key Reading Skill
(Use with Reading Workshop 2, p. 956)

Questioning

Do you ask questions as you read? You should. **Questioning** is a good way to check your understanding. It's easy enough to do. Just ask: Who? What? Where? When? How? Then reread or read ahead to find answers.

ACTIVITY

As you read "All Together Now" on page 960, ask questions and list them in the chart below. As you reread or read ahead, write answers to your questions. Try to ask and answer at least three questions.

Questions I Have	What I Found Out

Active Reading Graphic Organizer

(Use with Reading Workshop 2, p. 960)

"All Together Now"

In "All Together Now," Barbara Jordan says that tolerance is the way to make positive relationships between races. Use the web below to explain how and why, according to Jordan, people should act with tolerance. Look for details to write in the web as you read the selection.

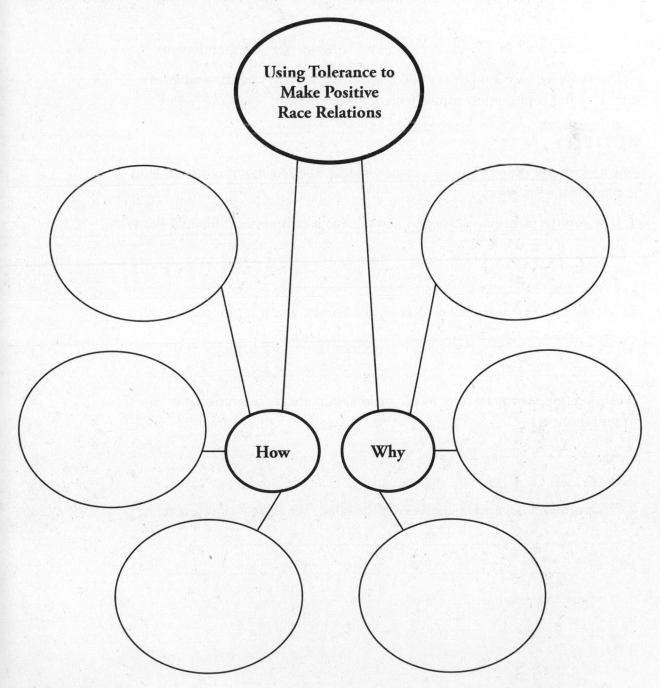

Grammar Practice
(Use with Grammar Link, p. 965)

Semicolons

You can use a **semicolon** in place of a comma and coordinating conjunction to join two independent clauses to make a compound sentence.

> We are going to the grocery store, **and** we will buy peaches.
> (comma and coordinating conjunction)
>
> OR
>
> We are going to the grocery store; we will buy peaches. (semicolon)

When sentences are long or contain contrasting ideas, a comma and a coordinating conjunction can help clarify the sentence.

ACTIVITY

Rewrite each pair of sentences as a single sentence. Add semicolons or conjunctions to combine the sentences.

1. The Smiths went on vacation. They went to a campground for a week.

_____

_____

2. Mara checked out three books from the library. She may not read them.

_____

_____

3. Turkey soup is my favorite meal. Turkey soup always reminds me of my grandmother.

_____

_____

4. We put tomatoes and cucumbers in the salad. We can't wait to eat it.

_____

_____

Literary Analysis
(Use with Reading Workshop 2, p. 967)

Point of View in Nonfiction

The perspective from which a real-life story is told is called **point of view.** In **first-person** point of view, an author uses "I" or "me" to describe the events as he or she views them. In **third-person** point of view, the author uses a nameless narrator to tell the events of the story.

ACTIVITY

Rewrite the passage below in first-person point of view.

  This was Pauline's very first Independence Day celebration. When she heard that her aunt would be taking her to a picnic and fireworks show, Pauline was thrilled. There would be many of the American foods she had heard so much about—hot dogs, corn on the cob, root beer. There would also be games and a rock band. In her country, she lived far from the city and did not get to experience new things very often. Pauline was also a little nervous about the fireworks. She knew that they would be loud. Would something catch fire? As she got ready to go, Pauline's nervousness gave way to excitement. This would certainly be a celebration worth writing home about.

_____

_____

_____

_____

_____

_____

_____

_____

_____

_____

_____

Active Reading Graphic Organizer
(Use with Reading Workshop 2, p. 968)

from *Through My Eyes*

In *Through My Eyes,* Ruby Bridges tells you the true story about her experience as a young girl during the fight to end discrimination. One section of the excerpt is from *The New York Times,* one is from Ruby Bridges' point of view, and another is told from Barbara Henry's position. Use the graphic organizer below to list descriptions of the officials, onlookers, and the school as told from the different standpoints. You may not be able to fill in all of the boxes.

	Description of the Officials	Description of the Onlookers	Description of the School
New York Times			
Ruby Bridges			
Barbara Henry			

Grammar Practice
(Use with Grammar Link, p. 975)

Semicolons with Conjunctive Adverbs

Join two independent clauses by placing a **semicolon** before a conjunctive adverb and a **comma** after the conjunctive adverb.

    Example: We will get the mail; **however,** we will wait to open it.

Conjunctive Adverbs: *therefore, thus, consequently, however, otherwise, still, besides, furthermore, moreover*

ACTIVITY

Rewrite each sentence. Make sure that you add semicolons and commas where they are needed.

1. We have plenty of homework therefore we should study tonight.

_____

_____

2. You can watch your sister otherwise you can come with me.

_____

_____

3. George had plenty of chores to do however he chose to play video games.

_____

_____

4. We were running behind schedule consequently we missed the boarding time for our flight.

_____

_____

5. I don't think that students should have to wear uniforms at school furthermore I think that uniforms stifle creativity.

_____

_____

Key Reading Skill

(Use with Reading Workshop 3, p. 976)

Reviewing

Skilled readers take time to **review** during and after reading. They know that going over what they've read can help them recall important information later on. Here are some ways to review:

- Pause to think about main ideas or key points.
- Take notes on your reading.
- Organize your notes in a graphic organizer, chart, or outline.

ACTIVITY

Reread "On Top of the World" on page 32. Then organize the main ideas and details you want to remember in the outline below. The outline has been started for you.

I. The Quest for the Top

    A. Mountain named after George Everest

        1. Honors his work mapping the Himalayas

        2. Tallest mountain in world (29,035 feet)

    B. Many adventurers want to climb Mount Everest

        1. _____

        2. _____

II. One Mean Mountain

    A. _____

        1. _____

        2. _____

    B. _____

III. It's Still There

    A. _____

        1. _____

    B. _____

        1. _____

Literary Analysis

(Use with Reading Workshop 3, p. 979)

Author's Bias

Author's bias is a type of persuasive writing that is one-sided. The author only presents his or her opinion or viewpoint. To spot a biased author, think about the following:

- Are you presented with only one side of a story or an issue?
- Does the author exaggerate, not provide facts to back up an opinion, or make broad, general statements?
- Does the author belong to a group that might make him or her biased?

ACTIVITY

Read the following paragraph from "A Letter to Senator Edwards." Then answer the questions about author bias.

> Bill 347.9 discriminates against young drivers. Don't licensed drivers over the age of eighteen also commit moving violations? Yet no one is suggesting that they get restricted licenses. There is no evidence that speeding or running a red light is a greater safety danger when the driver is under eighteen. People can be safe or reckless drivers regardless of their age. They don't automatically become better drivers once they reach eighteen. The same rules should apply to drivers of all ages.

1. Are you only presented with one side of the argument? If yes, what is it? If not, what are the two sides?

   _____

2. Does the author use facts to support his or her opinion?

   _____

3. Does the author make any broad, general statements or exaggeration? If yes, give an example. If not, explain why the paragraph does not contain any examples.

   _____

   _____

4. Does the author belong to a group that makes him or her biased?

   _____

Active Reading Graphic Organizer
(Use with Reading Workshop 3, p. 980)

"The Trouble with Television"

In "The Trouble with Television," Robert MacNeil points out a number of problems he thinks are caused by watching too much television. List four of them in the boxes below.

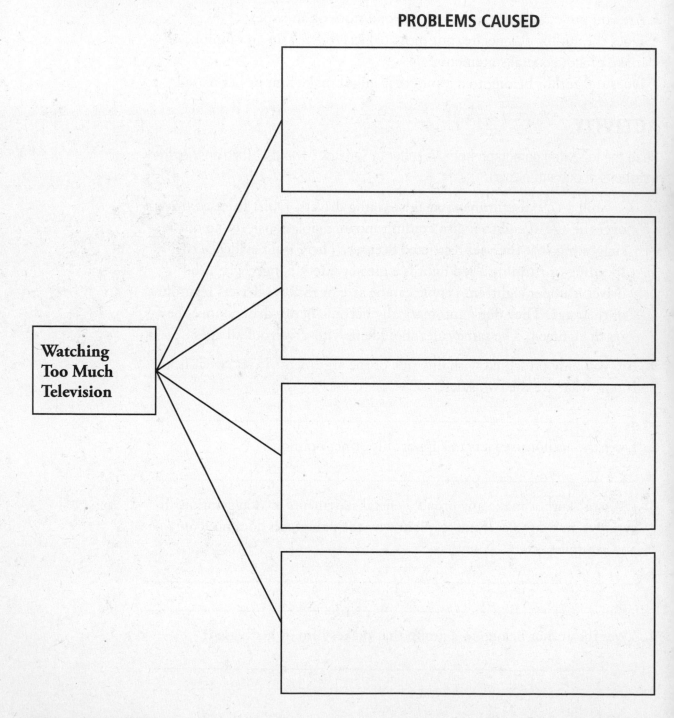

PROBLEMS CAUSED

Watching Too Much Television

Grammar Practice
(Use with Grammar Link, p. 985)

Quotation Marks

Use **quotation marks** to enclose the exact words of a speaker.

A **direct quote** gives the exact words that a person used.

> **Direct quote:** Felix said, "Come home now!"

An **indirect quote** tells what a person said without using the exact words.

> **Indirect quote:** Felix said to come home now.

ACTIVITY

Rewrite the following sentences as direct quotes.

1. The children whispered that they were waiting to surprise Cameron.

_____

_____

2. She said that my uniform was too wrinkly.

_____

_____

3. Samantha asked Fred whether he agreed with the argument.

_____

_____

4. Holly exclaimed that this was the best vacation ever.

_____

_____

5. George said that he was moving to Chicago.

_____

_____

6. Stephen asked Jeremy if he was going to see the movie on Friday.

_____

_____

Active Reading Graphic Organizer
(Use with Reading Workshop 3, p. 988)

"Teen Curfews"

The author of "Teen Curfews" reports on Anna Sale's fight to protect teen rights. Use this timeline to chart the main events in her struggle. Then give your opinion of the issue by answering the question that follows.

December 1997 _____
_____
_____
_____

March 1998 _____
_____
_____
_____

July 1998 _____
_____
_____
_____

July 2000 _____
_____
_____
_____

Do you agree with the courts or with Anna? Explain your response.

_____
_____
_____
_____
_____

Grammar Practice
(Use with Grammar Link, p. 991)

More Quotation Marks

- A direct quotation that is divided by a phrase is called a split quotation.

  Example: "Before you go," she explained, "you need to turn off the lights."

- Place a period, exclamation point, or question mark *inside* a quotation if the punctuation ends the quotation.

  Example: I asked, "Barbara, are you waiting for me?"

- Place an exclamation point or question mark *outside* the quotation mark if the punctuation ends the thought of the entire sentence.

  Example: Are you sure her exact words were, "Please leave now"?

- **Quotation Marks and Titles:** Use quotation marks around titles of shorter works.

ACTIVITY

Write a sentence that fits each description

1. Direct quotation

_____

_____

2. Split quotation

_____

_____

3. A quotation that is a question

_____

_____

4. A sentence that includes the title of a short story

_____

_____

Listening and Speaking
(Use with Writing Workshop Part 2, p. 995)

Deliver a Persuasive Speech

Speeches for election to office or in support of an issue often contain the same persuasive techniques used in advertising. For example, to be elected, a person must "sell" his or her ideas as the ideas that will be best for everyone.

ACTIVITY

Imagine that you are running for school office or want a change at your school or in your community. Write a short speech to persuade others to vote for you or to support your cause. In your speech, use at least three of the persuasive techniques listed on page 995.

Use the organizer below to plan your speech. After listing your topic, main points, and supporting details, write sentences to include in your speech that are examples of the persuasive techniques listed.

Topic:
Main Points:
Supporting Details:
Persuasive Techniques
Emotional Appeals
Testimonial
Transfer
Repetition
Exaggeration
Bandwagon

Deliver the speech to your class and see whether your classmates can identify the techniques you've used.

Viewing and Representing
(Use with Writing Workshop Part 2, p. 995)

Analyze a Television Commercial

Persuasion is based on the use of techniques. Appeals to emotion and testimonials are common techniques. Appeals to emotion involve words, sounds, or images that create strong feelings. Testimonials involve having someone famous and influential recommend a certain product or service. Appeals to emotion and use of testimonials are common in advertising, such as television commercials. Informed viewers can identify these appeals in commercials and decide whether they are used responsibly.

ACTIVITY

Analyze two television commercials using the questions in the chart below. Choose one that uses emotional appeals and one that uses testimonial.

Appeals to Emotion	Testimonial
Product:	**Product:**
• Which images catch my interest? What feelings do they create?	• Who is recommending this product or service? Why does this person do so?
• Which words suggest feelings? What feelings do they suggest?	• What reasoning does the person use?
• Are the appeals straightforward? Or do they reflect a "hidden agenda"—an attempt to manipulate the audience?	• Is the reasoning supported with facts, statistics, or other solid evidence? List the evidence.

Key Reading Skill

(Use with Reading Workshop 4, p. 998)

Clarifying

You're reading, and suddenly you realize you don't understand something. Sound familiar? Take some time to **clarify,** or clear up, what's confusing. Try these techniques to clarify passages:

• Reread the confusing parts slowly and carefully.
• "Talk out" the part to yourself.
• Look up unfamiliar words.
• Diagram relationships between ideas.

ACTIVITY

Reread "The Trouble with Television" on page 980. On the lines below, copy a passage you found confusing. Then, explain how you clarified it.

_____
_____
_____
_____
_____
_____
_____
_____
_____
_____
_____
_____
_____
_____
_____
_____

Literary Analysis
(Use with Reading Workshop 4, p. 1001)

Faulty Reasoning

Faulty reasoning is a kind of persuasion that is flawed, or has mistakes in it. Some faulty reasoning is done on purpose, such as reasoning in advertisements that is used to persuade you to buy a product. Here are some different kinds of faulty reasoning:

- **Either/Or Fallacy:** only two options are presented when there may be several more
- **Faulty Cause and Effect:** believing that one event causes another event to happen, but, in reality, the two events may be unrelated
- **Bandwagon:** thinking that something is the "right thing to do" because it is popular

ACTIVITY

Read each of the following passages. First, identify which kind of faulty reasoning is being used. Then, write a question or two that will help you make your conclusion. For example, if someone tries to persuade you to cut class by saying that everyone else is doing it, one question you can ask is "Is everyone else really cutting class?" Answering this question helps you understand that this person is using bandwagon reasoning.

1. I would not have been late to school this morning if my mother hadn't forgotten to remind me what time it was.

   _____

   _____

2. Most of us copy homework from one another; it's too hard to finish on our own. It's only homework, so it doesn't matter if we copy.

   _____

   _____

3. You can join the Spirit Club and become popular, or you can spend the rest of your school year being considered a loser and a geek.

   _____

   _____

Active Reading Graphic Organizer
(Use with Reading Workshop 4, p. 1002)

"Rally for Better Food, student flyer and poster"

When you are fighting for a cause, it helps to have many people on your side. The students who made the flyer and the poster in this selection knew this. In the chart below, identify the message in each document and the feelings or emotions the students used to try to get people to join them. Then answer the question that follows.

Flyer	
Message	**Feelings or Emotions**

Poster	
Message	**Feelings or Emotions**

After examining the details in your organizer, which document do you think is more effective? Why?

_____

_____

_____

_____

_____

Grammar Practice

(Use with Grammar Link, pp. 1005 or 1017)

Dashes

- Use **dashes** to set off long, explanatory phrases.

    The flowers we ordered—roses, daisies, petunias, and snapdragons— will all look great in the garden.

- Use a **dash** to set off a sudden break in thought.

    The flowers that we ordered—all of which are lovely—should arrive tomorrow afternoon.

ACTIVITY

Rewrite the following paragraph. Add dashes wherever they are needed.

    Lydia looked out over the lake she had eyes like a hawk and spotted the sailboat before anyone else did. She raised her binoculars to get a better view. She could see three figures Tom, Pascha, and Edward waving excitedly from the prow.

_____

_____

_____

_____

Parentheses

Use **parentheses** in place of commas to include extra information, to add a reflection, or to include an afterthought.

    Example: Dinner tonight (especially the steak) was delicious.

ACTIVITY

Rewrite each sentence, adding a phrase in parentheses.

1. My favorite book is full of adventure and excitement.

_____

2. American pioneers faced challenging journeys.

_____

Active Reading Graphic Organizer
(Use with Reading Workshop 4, p. 1008)

"Stop the Sun"

In "Stop the Sun," Terry struggles to understand what is going on with his father. Answer the questions in the sequence ladder below to record the events of Terry's struggle.

What does Terry want to know about his father? Why?

What happens at the mall?

How does Terry fight for his relationship with his father?

Does this solve his father's problem? Explain your response.

Does this solve Terry's problem? Explain your response.

Reading Across Texts Graphic Organizer
(Use with Reading Across Texts Workshop, p. 1018)

In persuasive writing, the writer tries to get you to think or act in a certain way. The writer does this by using persuasive techniques, such as emotional and ethical appeals. When you read a piece of persuasive writing, it is important to pay attention to the details that the writer gives to support his or her position.

ACTIVITY

Read "Teens Tackle Pollution in Their Communities" and "A Change in Climate." What is the position of each writer? What supporting details do the writers provide to defend their positions? Use the chart below to answer these questions.

	"Teens Tackle Pollution in Their Communities"	"A Change in Climate"
Position		
Supporting Reason		
Supporting Reason		
Supporting Reason		

Planning for the Unit Challenge
(Use with Wrap-Up, p. 1034)

A. Group Activity: Make a Mural

During the brainstorm session, use this chart to organize your group's ideas. As you identify each person, list what that person did to fight for what is right. That way you'll have ideas for how to depict them later when you draw your mural.

Person	What He or She Did to Fight for What Is Right

Try this tip to help you plan each person's placement on the mural during the sketching process. Cut one or two sheets of paper into four pieces and sketch each person on a different piece. Then, move the pieces around on your poster board until your group finds the arrangement that it likes best.

Planning for the Unit Challenge
(Use with Wrap-Up, p. 1035)

B. Solo Activity: Propose a Change

Place the most important change you wish to make in your school or community in the center circle of this web. Fill in the rest of the web to identify how you can make the change, who can help you, and any obstacles you'll face.

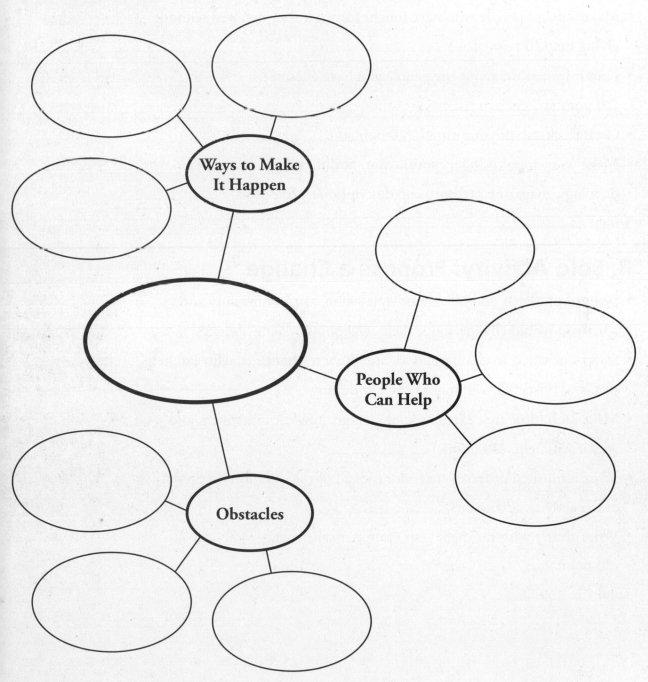

Assessment Rubrics for the Unit Challenge *(Use with Wrap-Up, pp. 1034–1035)*

You will be expected to satisfy the following standards in your group or solo activity:

A. Group Activity: Make a Mural

• Work effectively with others in a group setting. (20 points) _____

• Make a list of people who have fought for what they believed without giving up. (20 points) _____

• Find information about the people you have chosen. (20 points) _____

• Create a sketch of your mural. (20 points) _____

• Make your mural using a combination of different media, such as drawings, magazine pictures, and descriptions. (20 points) _____

Total: _____

B. Solo Activity: Propose a Change

• Write about what you like about your school and community and what you would change about them. (20 points) _____

• Select one thing to change and identify how to change it, who can help you, and obstacles you might face. (20 points) _____

• Make an outline that explains your change, how it can happen, and why it will help. (20 points) _____

• Write a finished proposal that addresses all of the questions in Step 4 of the activity. (20 points) _____

• Write clearly with no spelling or grammatical errors. (20 points) _____

Total: _____

Wrapping Up the Unit Challenge
(Use with Wrap-Up, pp. 1034–1035)

In Unit 7 you learned about people who have fought for what they believed in. Think about the insights you have gained from the Big Question. Express some of that knowledge in a new way. You could write a personal essay about yourself or someone close to you that uses facts and opinions to convey your message, as Ruby Bridges did in "Through My Eyes." You could write a persuasive piece to convert your reader to your point of view on an issue, as Robert MacNeil did in "The Trouble with Television." Be creative. Write your response below. Continue on another sheet of paper if you need more room.

_____

_____

_____

_____

_____

_____

_____

_____

_____

_____

_____

_____

_____

_____

_____

_____

_____

_____

_____

_____

Unit Vocabulary Review

ACTIVITY

Write a story using at least eight of the vocabulary words from the Word Bank. Your story could be about something you feel is worth fighting for or an issue that is important to you. Make sure that you use the vocabulary words correctly.

Word Bank		
nutritious	skeptically	optimist
controversial	passively	harmonious
violating	taunts	indispensable
convictions	distribution	persistence

_____

_____

_____

_____

_____

_____

_____

_____

_____

_____

_____

_____

_____

_____

_____

_____

_____

_____

Unit Vocabulary Review

ACTIVITY

Circle the word or phrase that best defines each underlined vocabulary word in the sentences.

1. Many students at the grade school were <u>illiterate</u>.

   A. uneducated   **B.** unprepared   **C.** untidy

2. Lynn <u>foundered</u> when she heard the horrible news.

   A. collapsed   **B.** hesitated   **C.** waited

3. Many children are <u>vulnerable</u> to disease and malnutrition.

   A. quick to act   **B.** likely to resist   **C.** exposed to danger

4. The factory did <u>emit</u> dangerous pollutants into the air.

   A. supply   **B.** give off   **C.** measure

5. The watch that Logan purchased at the vendor was <u>bogus</u>.

   A. not real   **B.** not special   **C.** not clean

6. The <u>perpetual</u> movement of the ocean waves was hypnotizing.

   A. done accidentally   **B.** moving quickly   **C.** continuing forever

7. <u>Virtually</u> everyone at the party was wearing jeans.

   A. actively   **B.** nearly   **C.** friendly

8. We need to <u>accumulate</u> enough money to go on the class trip.

   A. gather   **B.** finish   **C.** open

English Language Coach Review
(Use with English Language Coach, pp. 932 or 1006)

Denotation and Connotation

Denotation is the literal dictionary meaning of a word. That same word's **connotation** is the feeling or imagery that the word produces for a reader.

Many words may have either a positive or a negative connotation, depending on the image or feeling that the word creates. Think of a positive connotation as one that creates a "nicer" feeling or image than a negative connotation for a word that has a similar denotation.

- **Positive:** Joanna was surprised to see such *confusion*.
- **Negative:** Joanna was surprised to see such *chaos*.

ACTIVITY

Complete the chart below. The left column contains words with positive connotations. In the right column, write a word that has a similar meaning to the word in the left column but has a negative connotation. The first one has been done for you.

Positive Connotation	Negative Connotation
1. curious	nosy
2. self-confident	
3. inactive	
4. aggressive	
5. thrifty	

Read each sentence below. Circle the word in parentheses that has a positive connotation.

1. The (cook/chef) prepared a five-course meal.

2. The insects we saw were (fascinating/weird).

3. The girl answered the door with a (grin/smirk) on her face.

4. The car he drove on our date was (old/an antique).

5. Members of the drama club have (reminded/nagged) us several times about the meeting.

Academic Vocabulary Review

(Use with Academic Vocabulary, pp. 933, 956, 976, and 998)

Matching Meaning

Say each of the academic vocabulary words aloud. Then review the ways in which you used these words in the unit.

- In Reading Workshop 1, you learned that readers can be persuaded by an **ethical** appeal.
- In Reading Workshop 2, you determined whether or not an author's argument was **valid.**
- In Reading Workshop 3, you practiced reviewing text to find important **concepts.**
- In Reading Workshop 4, you learned to **clarify** to make difficult passages more clear.

Each item provides three clues to help you find the matching vocabulary word: the number of syllables, the part of speech, and the definition. Before you begin the activity, identify one or two of these categories for each word. Then, you can look at each item and select the one that matches.

Filling in the Blanks

Warm up by writing a sentence using each of the vocabulary words. Then, take turns reading each sentence with a partner, omitting the vocabulary word. Identify which vocabulary word fits in each sentence.

Complete this exercise with the same partner you worked with in the warm-up. Each word is used only one time in the activity. This should help you eliminate choices. When you have completed the activity, swap answers with a nearby pair to check for incorrect responses.

Academic Vocabulary Review

(Use with Academic Vocabulary, pp. 933, 956, 976, and 998)

ethical	valid	concepts	clarify

In this unit, you have used three **academic vocabulary** words: *ethical, valid, concepts,* and *clarify.* Use what you know about each word to complete the following activities.

ACTIVITY: Matching

Draw a line from each vocabulary word to its description.

1. two-syllable plural noun meaning organized thoughts   valid

2. three-syllable adjective having to do with standards of behavior   ethical

3. three-syllable verb meaning to make clear   concepts

4. two-syllable adjective having to do with logic and correct information   clarify

ACTIVITY: Filling in the Blanks

Fill in the blanks with the correct vocabulary word. There is only one correct answer for each blank space.

1. Ron decided to _____ as he read, to make the confusing passages more understandable.

2. To prepare for the test, Mika decided to review each selection to find the important _____ .

3. My teacher pointed out that it was not _____ , or acceptable, to present my opinions as facts in the essay I had written.

4. After asking herself questions about what she just read, Hilary decided that the author's logical argument was _____ .

Spelling and Handwriting Practice
(Use with Language Handbook, pp. R43–R44)

Spelling Rules for Forming Compound Words

A **compound word** is a new word that is formed when two complete words
are joined together. Compound words are not formed with prefixes or
suffixes. When you form a compound word, keep the original spelling of
both words.

thumb + tack = thumbtack   news + paper = newspaper

ACTIVITY

Use the following words to form as many compound words as you can. There may
be more than one way to combine some words. Check a dictionary if you are unsure
that the word you formed is a true compound word.

bag	bed	box	brow	bud	bug	clip	color
copper	eye	finger	flower	hand	head	lady	lid
line	nail	news	nose	paper	pig	print	sand
shake	stand	storm	tack	tail	thumb	time	wire

_____   _____

_____   _____

_____   _____

_____   _____

_____   _____

_____   _____

_____   _____

_____   _____

_____   _____

Spelling and Handwriting Practice
Handwriting

When you write, do not join the letters before and after the apostrophe in a contraction. Your strokes should be smooth and flowing, with smooth and even joining strokes.

ACTIVITY

Rewrite the following sentences. Change each underlined word to a contraction.

1. Joan <u>cannot</u> believe that Michael <u>will not</u> play in the band.

_____

2. <u>Do not</u> answer me in that tone of voice, or you <u>will not</u> go to the game.

_____

3. Her mother <u>could not</u> understand what the speaker was saying, so <u>she will</u> have to figure it out on her own.

_____

4. <u>They will</u> be sorry that they <u>did not</u> join the volunteers at the town center.

_____

5. It <u>does not</u> appear that Mabel will be joining us; perhaps she <u>could not</u> take time off work.

_____

6. I <u>would not</u> worry about the barking dog. Its bark is worse than its bite.

_____

7. She <u>cannot</u> write her letters perfectly until <u>she is</u> allowed to sharpen her pencil.

_____

8. <u>Will not</u> you wait until <u>we are</u> finished eating lunch?

_____

9. You <u>should not</u> go outside without your shoes.

_____

10. Practicing your handwriting <u>will not</u> necessarily help your spelling skills.

_____

Unit 7 Answer Key

Unit Introduction (p. 2)

1. Responses will vary. Students may say that fighting for a principle means standing up for your values and beliefs. They should highlight an example in which someone stood up for his or her principles.
2. Responses will vary. Students may say that living up to principles means acting on your principles in your everyday life. This could be more difficult than fighting for your principles because living up to your principles is constant; it's something you must do on a daily basis.
3. Students' responses will vary, but they should focus on students' interpretations of the opening quotation.

The Big Question—School to Home (pp. 3–6)

What is worth it?
Responses will vary. Responses should include examples of values that are worth fighting for and examples of values that are not worth fighting for.

Changes
Responses will vary. Students should record adult responses.

Principles to Live By
Responses will vary. Charts should include a reason for each value listed as important. Students should summarize the values in original mottos.

Key Reading Skill (p. 9)

Distinguishing Fact from Opinion
Possible responses:
Statement 1: opinion; I found the following evidence against this statement in the article: it's been practiced for over 35,000 years; 40 million Americans have at least one tattoo; it was the sixth fastest growing retail venture in United States in 1990s.
Statement 2: fact; I found the following information in the article to support this fact: decoration in some cultures; sign of rank; mark special occasion; clan membership; evidence of adventures.

Statement 3: fact; I found the following instances where tattooing was used to dehumanize people: ancient Greece: slaves; ancient Rome: criminals; Nazis: prisoners at concentration camps.
Statement 4: opinion; The article contains the names of various young people and older people with tattoos.
Statement 5: opinion; The information on page 394 of the article under #4 supports some risk, but there is no evidence provided that states that it's *always* risky.

Literary Analysis (p. 10)

Persuasive Appeals
Possible responses:
Emotional Appeals: "If Mom or Dad is always in the car, playing the role of 'back-seat driver,' how will a young person ever learn to drive independently out on the road?"
Ethical Appeals: "Let's not pass new laws that discriminate against drivers under eighteen."
Appeals to Logic: "There is no evidence that speeding or running a red light is a greater safety danger when the driver is under eighteen."

Active Reading Graphic Organizer (p. 11)

"Saving Water: Why Save Something That Covers Two-thirds of the Earth?"
Possible responses:
Fresh water on Earth is found in lakes and rivers.
From there, it goes to treatment plants.
There, bleach is used to clean the water.
From there it's piped to your house.
Where it's used for cooking, washing, etc.
To get warm, it goes through the hot water heater.
It leaves your house through sewage pipes.
And returns to the treatment plant.

Grammar Practice (p. 12)

Colons to Introduce Items
1. Send a memo to the following people: Smith, Jones, Harris, and Johnson.
2. Our trip will include swimming, boating, and fishing.
3. Bring a sleeping bag, a tent, a blanket, and boots.

Colons to Separate

1. The following time slots are open: 2:00 to 4:00 and 5:30 to 7:30.
2. Devon said that we would eat dinner at 7:00.
3. The party began at one o'clock? We thought that it began at 2:00.

Active Reading Graphic Organizer (p. 13)

from *The Measure of Our Success*

Lesson 1: There is no free lunch. **Possible response:** She was taught that the world, and blacks in particular, had a lot of problems, but that she could change them and no one else was going to do it for her.

Lesson 2: Assign yourself. **Possible response:** Her father had a playground and canteen built behind the church for the black church and community members to use.

Lesson 3: Never work just for money. **Possible response:** She was taught that nothing was too lowly to do and to use her head and her hands.

Lesson 4: Do not be afraid of taking risks. **Possible response:** Her parents took risks by building black-only services in the segregated South.

Lesson 5: Take parenting and family life seriously. **Possible response:** Her parents were serious about her education; her father excused her from chores if she was reading.

Lesson 6: Remember that fellowship of human beings is more important than fellowship of race, class, and gender. **Possible response:** Her elders told her that as a "child of God," no one could look down on her and she couldn't look down on anyone else.

Lesson 7: Listen for "the sound of the genuine" within yourself. **Possible response:** She was inspired by Sojourner Truth's story.

Lesson 8: Never think life is not worth living or that you cannot make a difference. **Possible response:** Her parents opened a home for the elderly, which instilled the idea that even the very old are worthy and can make a difference in the community. She learned that everyone was her neighbor.

Writing Workshop Graphic Organizer (p. 14)

Responses will vary. Each chart should include a topic, a position statement, and at least three supporting details.

Grammar Practice (p. 15)

Apostrophes

1. The tree's leaves fell around its trunk.
2. I don't understand how the dog's leash got tangled.
3. The apple's skin had bruises all over it.

Key Reading Skill (p. 16)

Questioning

Responses will vary. Students should write at least three questions and use what they have read to answer them.

Active Reading Graphic Organizer (p. 17)

"All Together Now"

Possible responses:

How: start small; have one friend with a different background than yours; bring people together; parents encourage their children to be tolerant

Why: to keep people from feeling excluded; to learn about those who are different than us; to develop a broader view of humanity; to learn to care about other human beings

Grammar Practice (p. 18)

Semicolons

1. The Smiths went on vacation; they went to a campground for a week.
2. Mara checked out three books from the library, but she may not read them.
3. Turkey soup is my favorite meal; it always reminds me of my grandmother.
4. We put tomatoes and cucumbers in the salad; we can't wait to eat it.

Literary Analysis (p. 19)

Point of View in Nonfiction

Possible response:

This will be my very first Independence Day celebration. When I found out my aunt would be taking me to a picnic and fireworks show, I was thrilled. There will be many of the American foods I have heard so much about—hot dogs, corn on the cob, root beer. There will also be games and a rock band. In my country, I lived far from the city and did not get to experience new things very often. But I'm also a little nervous about the fireworks. I know that they will be loud. What if something catches fire? Well, even though I'm a little nervous, I am so excited. This certainly will be a celebration worth writing home about.

Active Reading Graphic Organizer (p. 20)

from *Through My Eyes*

Possible responses:

New York Times: **Description of the Officials:** black squad cars; gold-striped uniforms, black boots, and white crash helmets; Deputy federal marshals wearing yellow arm bands; **Description of the Onlookers:** 150 whites, mostly housewives and teenage youths; chanting; onlookers jeered and shouted taunts; **Description of the School:** yellow brick building

Ruby Bridges: Description of the Officials: four serious-looking white men dressed in suits; policemen in uniforms; **Description of the Onlookers:** I thought maybe it was Mardi Gras . . .; people yelled and threw things; crowd outside was bigger and louder; they sang to "Battle Hymn of the Republic"; a woman threatens to poison her; **Description of the School:** it looked bigger and nicer than my old school; everyone was white; everyone was upset

Barbara Henry: Description of the Officials: the police could only protect the parking lot; you couldn't be confident of the New Orleans police's support or cooperation; **Description of the Onlookers:** N/A; **Description of the School:** N/A

Grammar Practice (p. 21)

Semicolons with Conjunctive Adverbs

1. We have plenty of homework; therefore, we should study tonight.
2. You can watch your sister; otherwise, you can come with me.
3. George had plenty of chores to do; however, he chose to play video games.
4. We were running behind schedule; consequently, we missed the boarding time for our flight.
5. I don't think that students should have to wear uniforms at school; furthermore, I think that uniforms stifle creativity.

Key Reading Skill (p. 22)

Reviewing

Possible response:
  I. The Quest for the Top
     A. Mountain named after George Everest
        1. Honors his work mapping the Himalayas
        2. Tallest mountain in world (29,035 feet)
     B. Many adventurers want to climb Mount Everest
        1. "Because it's there" (George Mallory)
        2. Almost 1,200 have made it to the top
 II. One Mean Mountain
     A. Threats to safety and health on Mount Everest
        1. Ice, snow, freezing wind cause frostbite
        2. Crevasses (deep cracks in ice)
     B. Everest can't really be conquered
III. It's Still There
     A. Mountain is less a mystery today than in 1953
        1. People have climbed from all sides and on 15 routes; high-tech equipment available
     B. Climb is still hard
        1. Inexperienced climbers hire guides; even with guides, can be risky

Literary Analysis (p. 23)

Author's Bias

Possible responses:

1. You are only presented with one side of the argument. The author believes that people of all ages should be punished for moving violations.
2. The author does not use any facts.
3. The author's statement that people of all ages can be reckless drivers may be considered a generalization.
4. From reading the entire letter, I know that the author is someone under eighteen. This makes the author part of a biased group because the law would directly affect him or her.

Active Reading Graphic Organizer (p. 24)

"The Trouble with Television"

Possible responses:

Problems Caused: TV keeps you from doing other things; TV discourages concentration; TV makes you a passive observer; TV makes information boring and dismissible; TV contributes to low literacy rates; TV reduces your appetite for complexity.

Grammar Practice (p. 25)

Quotation Marks

1. The children whispered, "We are waiting to surprise Cameron."
2. She said, "Your uniform is too wrinkly."
3. Samantha asked, "Fred, do you agree with the argument?"
4. Holly exclaimed, "That this was the best vacation ever!"
5. George said, "I am moving to Chicago."
6. Stephen asked, "Jeremy, are you going to see the movie on Friday?"

Active Reading Graphic Organizer (p. 26)

"Teen Curfews"

December 1997: The Charleston city council passed the Youth Protection Ordinance which placed a curfew on people under 18 years of age.
March 1998: Anna and the ACLU filed a lawsuit to overturn the ordinance.

July 1998: Anna and her friends testified in court about the discriminatory effects of the ordinance.
July 2000: The state supreme court upheld the law by a margin of 4 to 1.

Responses will vary. Students should take a side on the issue and provide logical support for their opinions.

Grammar Practice (p. 27)

More Quotation Marks

Possible responses:

1. "Here is your sweater," David said. (direct quotation)
2. "Tomorrow or the next day," Martina sighed, "the rain will finally stop." (split quotation)
3. "When will we go to the park?" Melvin asked. (quotation that is a question)
4. I loved the story "Rosenthal the Rascal" when I was young. (title of a short story)

Listening and Speaking (p. 28)

Topics and content of speeches will vary. Check students' organizers before they write their speeches to confirm that they understand the persuasive techniques and have generated relevant examples to include in their speeches.

Viewing and Representing (p. 29)

Possible responses:

Appeals to Emotion
Which images catch my interest? The people who seem much too happy driving a car; **What feelings do they create?** The images are depressing because they are so phony.
Which words suggest feelings? *New feeling, success;* **What feelings do they suggest?** Change, accomplishment
Are the appeals straightforward? They are implied through images. **Or do they reflect a "hidden agenda"—an attempt to manipulate the audience?** The commercial is straightforward because they want a viewer to buy a car.

Testimonial
Who is recommending this product or service? A famous athlete; **Why does this person do so?** He wears the clothes.
What reasoning does the person use? The clothes help him train.

Is the reasoning supported with facts, statistics, or other solid evidence? No, he gives only anecdotal information. List the evidence. He gives no facts, but his claim seems probable.

Key Reading Skill (p. 30)
Clarifying
Responses will vary. Students should select a difficult passage to clarify. Students may use one of the clarifying techniques listed on the page.

Literary Analysis (p. 31)
Faulty Reasoning
1. faulty cause and effect; **Possible response:** Did anything else cause you to be late? Are you sure that you wouldn't have been late even if your mother reminded you about the time? Were you late for another reason?
2. bandwagon; **Possible response:** Does it make it less wrong to copy because most students do it? Is it really harmless to copy someone else's homework rather than doing it yourself?
3. either/or fallacy; **Possible response:** Are these really the only two choices? Does not being in the Spirit Club automatically make you a loser? Does joining the Spirit Club automatically make you popular? Are there people who are not in the Spirit Club, but who are popular?

Active Reading Graphic Organizer (p. 32)
"Rally for Better Food, student flyer and poster"
Possible responses:
Flyer: Message: Come protest for better food.
Feelings or Emotions: angry, persuasive, demanding, rebellious
Poster: Come protest for better food. Feelings or Emotions: informative, humorous (with "Food Fight" and the play on words "Junk the Junk")

Responses will vary. Students should indicate which document they felt was more effective and should provide logical support for that point of view.

Grammar Practice (p. 33)
Dashes
Lydia looked out over the lake—she had eyes like a hawk—and spotted the sailboat before anyone else did. She raised her binoculars to get a better view. She could see three figures—Tom, Pascha, and Edward—waving excitedly from the prow.

Parentheses
Possible responses:
1. My favorite book (written by the author who wrote *Pirate Island*) is full of adventure and excitement.
2. American pioneers (the first Americans to travel West) faced challenging journeys.

Active Reading Graphic Organizer (p. 34)
"Stop the Sun"
Possible responses:
Rung 1: Terry wants to know why his father sometimes "disappears" because it scares him.
Rung 2: At the mall, Terry finds his father balled up and shaking in a corner, having an episode that is worse than usual.
Rung 3: Terry fights for his relationship with his father by asking him what happened in Vietnam, even though it scares Terry to do so.
Rung 4: It does not really solve his father's problem to share the story with Terry because his father's syndrome is too complicated to be fixed that easily.
Rung 5: It helps Terry because that day he gets some understanding of what happened in Vietnam and of what things difficult memories his father has.

Reading Across Texts Graphic Organizer (p. 35)
Possible responses:
"Teens Tackle Pollution in Their Communities":
Position: Young people can make a difference in protecting the environment.
Supporting Reason: Texas teenagers formed Don't Be Crude, a group that educates people about the dangers of improper fluid disposal.

Supporting Reason: High-school student Amir Nadav helped convince the state senate to pass a bill calling for reduced idling of school buses and an increase in the number of bus inspections.

Supporting Reason: Thirteen-year-old Gina Gallant invented a new material for paving roads that uses discarded plastic.

"A Change in Climate":

Position: Small changes in the climate can have a big impact on Earth's plants and animals.

Supporting Reason: Trees on mountaintops are growing at higher elevations.

Supporting Reason: Pollutants may be influencing global warming and causing the temperature to rise.

Supporting Reason: Animals that cannot adapt to climate change will experience a drastic decrease in population.

Planning for the Unit Challenge (pp. 36–39)

A. Group Activity: Make a Mural

Students should fill in the chart with the name of each person they have chosen and a description of how each person stood up for what was right. Before drawing the final mural, students should make sketches on individual pieces of paper and move the pieces around on the poster board to find their favorite arrangement.

B. Solo Activity: Propose a Change

Students' webs should identify the change they want to make, how they want to make it, people who can help, and obstacles they may face.

Wrapping Up the Unit Challenge

Students may use both facts and opinions in a personal essay to tell about an experience they have had fighting for what they believed in. Or they may write a persuasive piece attempting to convince the audience to agree with their point of view. They should clearly state the issue and convey their stance. Students should follow the conventions of standard written English.

Unit Vocabulary Review (pp. 40 and 41)

Responses will vary. Students' stories should include vocabulary words used correctly.

1. A
2. A
3. C
4. B
5. A
6. C
7. B
8. A

English Language Coach Review (p. 42)

Denotation and Connotation

Possible responses:

2. stubborn
3. lazy
4. pushy
5. cheap

1. chef
2. fascinating
3. grin
4. an antique
5. reminded

Academic Vocabulary Review (pp. 43 and 44)

Matching

1. concepts
2. ethical
3. clarify
4. valid

Filling in the Blanks

1. clarify
2. concepts
3. ethical
4. valid

Spelling and Handwriting Practice
(pp. 45 and 46)
Possible responses:
handbag, eyebrow, copperhead, handshake,
newsprint, thumbtack, timeline, fingernail,
thumbnail, pigpen, flowerbed, newsstand,
sandstorm, fingerprint

Handwriting
Be sure students' letters before and after the
apostrophe in the contractions are not joined.
  1. Joan can't believe that Michael won't play
     in the band.
  2. Don't answer me in that tone of voice, or you
     won't go to the game.
  3. Her mother couldn't understand what the
     speaker was saying, so she'll have to figure
     it out on her own.
  4. They'll be sorry that they didn't join the
     volunteers at the town center.
  5. It doesn't appear that Mabel will be joining
     us; perhaps she couldn't take time off work.
  6. I wouldn't worry about the barking dog. Its
     bark is worse than its bite.
  7. She can't write her letters perfectly until
     she's allowed to sharpen her pencil.
  8. Won't you wait until we're finished
     eating lunch?
  9. You shouldn't go outside without your shoes.
 10. Practicing your handwriting won't necessarily
     help your spelling skills.